THE SIMPSONS

For information address
Bongo Comics Group
P.O. Box 1963, Santa Monica, CA 90406-1963, USA

Published in the UK by Titan Books, a division of Titan Publishing Group Ltd,
144 Southwark St., London SE1 0UP, under licence from Bongo Entertainment, Inc and Matt Groening Productions, Inc..

FIRST EDITION: AUGUST 2011
ISBN: 9780857689023
1 3 5 7 9 10 8 6 4 2

Publisher: Matt Groening
Creative Director: Bill Morrison
Managing Editor: Terry Delegeane
Director of Operations: Robert Zaugh
Art Director: Nathan Kane
Art Director Special Projects: Serban Cristescu
Production Manager: Christopher Ungar
Assistant Art Director: Chia-Hsien Jason Ho
Production/Design: Karen Bates, Nathan Hamill, Art Villanueva
Staff Artist: Mike Rote
Administration: Ruth Waytz, Pete Benson
Legal Guardian: Susan A. Grode

Contributing Artists:
Karen Bates, John Costanza, Mike DeCarlo, Serban Cristescu, Alan Hellard,
Nathan Kane, Mike Kazaleh, James Lloyd, Bill Morrison,Vinny Navarrette, Phil Ortiz, Patrick Owsley, Mike Rote, Howard
Shum, Robert Stanley, Carlos Valenti, Art Villanueva
Contributing Writers:
James W. Bates, Chuck Dixon, Earl Kress,
Mary Trainor, Patric C. W. Verrone, Patric M. Verrone

PRINTED IN CHINA

THE SIMPSONS

TITAN BOOKS

OFF THE GRID

JAMES W. BATES SCRIPT **PHIL ORTIZ** PENCILS **MIKE DECARLO** INKS **ROBERT STANLEY** COLORS **KAREN BATES** LETTERS **BILL MORRISON** EDITOR

AT THE BURNS MANSION...

LOOK AT ALL THAT ELECTRICITY! LIGHTS BURNING, HEATERS FIRING! ISN'T IT BEAUTIFUL?

I'D GO AS FAR AS TO SAY IT WAS ROMANTIC, SIR.

SHOW ME THE CHART AGAIN, SMITHERS.

EXCELLENT!

THIS COLD SNAP HAS REALLY FORCED YOUR CONSUMERS TO CRANK UP THEIR THERMOSTATS.

YES, AND IN THE WAKE OF THEIR GREEDY USE OF THE ENERGY I *SUPPLY*, I *DEMAND* A RAISE IN PRICES!

ALL THIS CHATTER ABOUT THE COLD HAS SENT A CHILL DOWN MY SPINE. SMITHERS, PUT ANOTHER LOG ON THE FIRE.

SIR, WOULD YOU LIKE TO BURN A LOG OF FIFTIES OR HUNDREDS?

THIS CAN'T BE RIGHT! HOW CAN THEY WANT THIS MUCH? I **WON'T** PAY IT!

BILL

I DON'T THINK WE **CAN** PAY IT.

WE CAN ALWAYS DIP INTO BART'S COLLEGE FUND.

BWAH-HA-HA-HA!!!

YOU KNOW EVERY TIME YOU MAKE THAT JOKE, MY SELF-ESTEEM DIES A LITTLE.

IT'S AWFUL THAT THEY'D BUMP UP PRICES IN THE WINTER WHEN PEOPLE NEED FUEL THE MOST.

NEXT WEEK, THERE'S A GREAT DOCUMENTARY AIRING. IT'S CALLED "PLANET ON PROBATION."

HUH, WHAT? SORRY, I FELL ASLEEP WHILE YOU WERE YAMMERING ABOUT SOME DOCUMENTARY.

YOU'LL SEE! THAT SHOW IS GOING TO EXPOSE HOW THE POWER COMPANIES MANIPULATE PRICES.

ZZZZZ!

WE HAVE TO DO SOMETHING ABOUT THESE BILLS.

WE CAN CUT OUR COSTS BY BECOMING MORE ENERGY CONSCIOUS.

CUTTING COSTS WON'T JUST HELP US, BUT IT'LL ALSO STICK IT TO THE MAN!

I LIKE THE SOUND OF THAT. WHAT DO WE HAVE TO DO?

IT'S SIMPLE...WE USE *LESS POWER*.

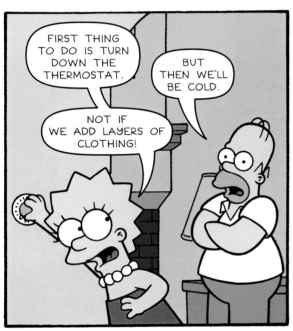

FIRST THING TO DO IS TURN DOWN THE THERMOSTAT.

BUT THEN WE'LL BE COLD.

NOT IF WE ADD LAYERS OF CLOTHING!

BUT SWEATERS DON'T COMPLIMENT MY FIGURE.

MMPHGGGH!

BART, SHUSH!

THIS SAYS THAT FOR EVERY ONE DEGREE WE LOWER THE THERMOSTAT THAT WE'LL SAVE FIVE PERCENT ON OUR HEATING BILL.

THE LATE GREAT OVERHEATED EARTH

FIVE PERCENT FOR EVERY DEGREE? I SAY WE TURN IT *ALL THE WAY OFF!*

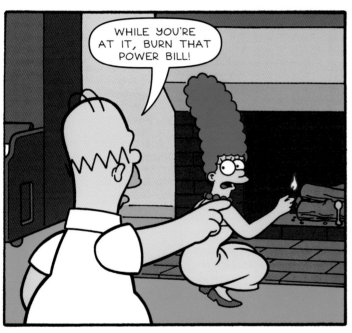

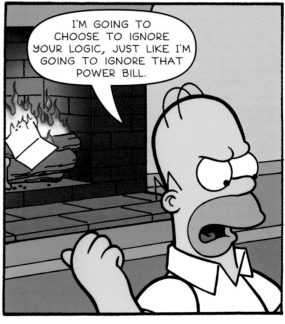

9

AS OF THIS MOMENT, THE SIMPSONS ARE GOING *OFF THE GRID!*

NO MORE BURNS HEAT! NO MORE BURNS ELECTRICITY! WE'RE GONNA LIVE POWER FREE AND GREEN!

I DON'T KNOW...

WE'RE GOING TO MAKE A STATEMENT!

YEAH..."HELP! WE'RE FREEZING TO DEATH!"

THIS IS A GREAT OPPORTUNITY TO SHOW EVERYONE HOW THEY CAN CONSERVE POWER AND STILL GET BY.

CLICK!

I GUESS IF WE'RE REALLY GOING TO DO THIS, WE BETTER BUNDLE UP.

WE *ARE* DOING THIS! MY RESOLVE IS STRONG!

RIGHT ON, DAD!

READING BY CANDLELIGHT! I FEEL LIKE LAURA INGALLS IN "THE LITTLE HOUSE ON THE PRAIRIE!"

THAT MUST BE NICE FOR YOU, BUT *I* FEEL LIKE A BAG OF FROZEN PEAS.

BART, I KNOW IT'S TOUGH, BUT TRY TO THINK WARM THOUGHTS.

I DON'T THINK I CAN LIVE ANOTHER MINUTE WITHOUT THE TV!

WAY TO STAY STRONG, HOMER.

HOMIE, IT'S ONLY BEEN FORTY-FIVE MINUTES.

THE LONGEST FORTY-FIVE MINUTES OF MY LIFE!

ALL ADDICTS GO THROUGH WITHDRAWAL.

I'M NOT ADDICTED TO TV. I'M COOL.

IF HOMER WAS ADDICTED, HE'D CARE THAT "THE WIDE WORLD OF WACKY MONKEYS" IS ON RIGHT NOW.

D'OH! I'M MISSING WACKY MONKEYS.

NEXT MORNING...

NO ALARM? WHAT TIME IS IT?

YOU'RE LATE FOR WORK!

I'M GONNA HAVE TO DRIVE THROUGH EVERY STOP SIGN AND RED LIGHT!

NO YOU WON'T!

I HAVE TO! IF I GET THERE TOO LATE, THE VENDING MACHINE SELLS OUT OF CINNAMON ROLLS.

YOU'RE FORGETTING SOMETHING.

MY PANTS!

THAT'S NOT ALL.

OF COURSE! A GOOD-BYE KISS!

YOU ARE FORGETTING OUR NEW ECO-FRIENDLY-POWER-INDEPENDENT LIFESTYLE. *NO DRIVING!*

HUFF-PUFF-HUFF-PUFF...

DAYS LATER...SUNDAY...

THAT WAS A VERY NICE SERMON, REVEREND LOVEJOY.

First Church of Springfield

TO EVERYTHING THERE IS A SEASON. AND IT'S THE SEASON TO TURN TURN TURN UP THE HEAT!

THANK YOU, MARGE.

YOUR HUSBAND MUST'VE MISSED THE PART ABOUT CLEANLINESS BEING NEXT TO GODLINESS.

HOMER REFUSES TO SHAVE WITHOUT HOT WATER.

I GUESS THAT GOES FOR *SHOWERING*, TOO.

BUT WHY DON'T YOU HAVE HOT WATER?

WE STOPPED USING ELECTRIC AND GAS.

BART TOLD ME THE OTHER DAY THAT YOU'VE BEEN LIVING OFF THE POWER GRID FOR A WEEK.

THE LONGEST WEEK OF MY LIFE!

I SAY "BRAVO!" YOU INSPIRED ME TO DO THE SAME THING.

INSPIRED YOU?

AND ME AS WELL!

YOU DON'T SAY?

GLAVIN! AFTER I HEARD ABOUT YOUR CAUSE, I STARTED MAKING WITH THE SOLAR PANELS AND THE WIND TURBINES. ENG-HEY!

SEE, MOM? I TOLD YOU WE WERE MAKING A REAL DIFFERENCE!

BY SHRINKING OUR CARBON FOOTPRINT, WE'RE DOING OUR PART TO SAVE THE PLANET.

IT'S A BLESSED THING. TRULY GOD'S WORK!

HEY, IT WAS **MY** IDEA!

GOOD ONE, HOMER. YOU'RE A HERO!

MMM... HERO. SUB. HOAGIE.

TURNING OFF THE POWER SOUNDS LIKE A GOOD WAY TO SHOW BURNS WHAT WE THINK OF HIM JACKING UP PRICES!

I SAY WE **ALL** GO OFF THE GRID!

YEAH!!!

SIR, DO YOU NEED MORE CAVIAR?

NO, THE BATH IS JUST FINE.

DID YOU WANT ME TO SCRUB YOUR BACK?

FOR THE UMPTEENTH TIME...NO!

I WANT TO SEE THE CHART!

WHY IS THE ARROW DROPPING LIKE A LEAD DIRIGIBLE?

USAGE IS DOWN.

POPPY-COCK! THE WEATHER OUTSIDE IS AS COLD AS ONE OF ELEANOR ROOSEVELT'S KISSES.

WORD IS THAT SOME OF YOUR COSTUMERS ARE REVOLTING AGAINST THE HIGHER RATES BY USING LESS OR NONE OF YOUR POWER!

OUTRAGEOUS!

SHOULD WE LOWER PRICES?

NEVER! WE'LL EXPLAIN TO THEM THAT WHAT THEY ARE DOING IS WRONG IN THE ONLY WAY THOSE INGRATES WILL UNDERSTAND...*AN INFOMERCIAL!*

TELEPHONE THOSE HOLLYWOOD WHIZ KIDS THAT PRODUCED MY DOCUMENTARY.

BART, THOSE ARE MY GREAT WOMEN IN HISTORY BOOKS! WHAT ARE YOU DOING?

I'M SAVING THE PLANET LIKE YOU WANTED ME TO!

THOSE WOMEN ARE *GREAT* AT KEEPING THE FIRE GOING.

JOAN OF ARC

STUPID ELECTRIC FLANDERS.

MOM'S RIGHT. THE GUYS AREN'T HANDLING THIS WELL AT ALL.

LISA, HELP ME WITH THE LAUNDRY.

IT'S GOING TAKE FOREVER TO COOK PORK CHOPS OVER A FIRE IN THE BACKYARD SO I NEED YOU TO WASH THE LAUNDRY BY WHACKING THE CLOTHES WITH THESE STONES.

YOUR FATHER'S UNDERWEAR MIGHT NEED A DOUBLE WHACKING.

TV LISTINGS. HMM...THAT REMINDS ME, WHEN DOES "PLANET ON PROBATION" AIR?

:GASP!: IT'S ON TONIGHT!

PLANET ON PROBATION

MEANWHILE, UPSTAIRS...

DAD, WHAT ARE YOU DOING HERE?

THE NINCOMPOOPS AT THE RETIREMENT CASTLE JOINED YOUR PROTEST AND TURNED OFF THE POWER.

BUT WHAT ARE YOU DOING *HERE*?

WITH NO POWER, THERE'S NO TV. AND WITHOUT TV, ALL ANYONE THERE WANTS TO DO IS TALK!

DO YOU KNOW HOW BORING IT IS TO LISTEN TO AN OLD PERSON YAMMER? LET ME TELL YOU ABOUT IT...

I THOUGHT I HEARD SOMEONE ARRIVE. GRAMPA'S HERE.

SO IS SOMEONE ELSE.

KNOCK! KNOCK! KNOCK!

WHAT'S GOING ON?

HOMER, WE WE'RE WITH YOU WHEN YOU STARTED THIS BOY-COTT, BUT NOW WE NEED TO GO BACK ON THE GRID.

WHAT ABOUT STICKIN' IT TO THE MAN?

WITHOUT THE REFRIGERATION UNIT, MY SQUISHIES DO NOT SQUISH.

NO ONE WANTS TO DRINK WARM BEER, EXCEPT GROUNDS-KEEPER WILLIE.

WITHOUT LIGHTS MY "HERB" GARDEN WON'T GROW!

WHY ARE YOU HERE?

BURNS TURNED OFF OL' GIL'S POWER A MONTH AGO. I JUST TAGGED ALONG TO BE NEAR PEOPLE WHO AREN'T TRYING TO REPOSSESS SOMETHING FROM ME.

WHADDYA THINK, HOMER? IS ALL THIS PAIN AND SUFFERING WORTH IT?

WORTH IT? I DON'T KNOW. AT FIRST, I WAS MAD ABOUT MY POWER BILL, BUT THEN LISA EXPLAINED HOW WE'RE SAVING THE PLANET! WE SHOULD TO LISTEN TO HER!

UM, DAD...

...LISTEN TO ME.

THAT'S WHAT I'M TELLING THEM TO DO, HONEY.

I THINK WE SHOULD TURN THE POWER BACK ON!

WHAT?

THE END

22

What's WASHING?

Five Springfield residents are washing their clothes – but can you figure out who from the clothes in these washing machines?

A

B

C

D

HOMER

BART

LISA

DISCO STU

ANSWERS: A: LISA, B: DISCO STU, C: BART, D: HOMER

CROSSWORD

TEST YOUR SIMPSONS KNOWLEDGE RIGHT HERE!

ACROSS

2 The street the Simpsons live on: _ _ _ _GREEN TERRACE (4)

4 Homer's favourite brand of beer. (4)

5 The Laundromat where the Simpsons do their washing. (4,1,4)

7 One of Homer's workmates at the Springfield Nuclear Power Plant: _ _ _ _ CARLSON (4)

8 Bart's arch-nemesis: SIDESHOW _ _ _ (3)

9 Grandpa Simpson's first name. (3)

11 The first name of Springfield's most famous action movie star: _ _ _ _ _ _ _ WOLFCASTLE (7)

13 Homer's favourite place to drink beer. (4)

14 Springfield's most notorious mobster: FAT _ _ _ _ (4)

DOWN

1 Springfield's fast-food restaurant chain owned by a certain clown. (6,6)

3 The surname of Bart's best friend. (3,6)

4 The owner of Stu's Disco. (5,3)

6 The surname of the Simpsons' next-door neighbours. (8)

10 A worker at Springfield Nuclear Power Plant and best friend of 7 ACROSS. (5)

12 The youngest child in the Flanders family. (4)

ANSWERS:
ACROSS: 2-EVER 4-DUFF 5-SUDS'N'DUDS 7-CARL 8-BOB 9-ABE 11-RAINIER 13-MOES 14-TONY
DOWN: 1-KRUSTY BURGER 3-VAN HOUTEN 4-DISCO STU 6-FLANDERS 10-LENNY 12-TODD

MATT GROENING

23

ONE YEAR LATER...

THE END

THE LANDFILL OF FORBIDDEN TOYS

CHUCK DIXON
SCRIPT

JOHN COSTANZA
PENCILS

HOWARD SHUM
INKS

ROBERT STANLEY
COLORS

KAREN BATES
LETTERS

BILL MORRISON
EDITOR

THIS NISCHTIK KNICK-KNACK? *THIS* IS YOUR BEST SHOT?

JUST A CHEAP ACTION FIGURE, RIGHT? BUT ADD *WATER* AND...

...STAND BY FOR SUPER-HYDRO-ACTION KRUSTY!

YEEEK!

WOW!

SPROING!

THE LITTLE IDIOTS WILL *PLOTZ* FOR THIS!

EEP?

WE'LL SELL *MILLIONS!* *BILLIONS!*

ENVIRONMENTAL PROTECTION AGENCY!

NOBODY MOVE!

PACK THIS STUFF UP! IT'S *ALL* TAINTED!

TAINTED?

THESE PLAYTHINGS ARE ALL ECOLOGICAL *VIOLATIONS!*

LIKE *WHAT?*

DIOXINS, CHLORIDES, ANIMAL FECES, MERCURY, LIKELIHOOD OF ELECTRICAL SHOCK, FIRE HAZARDS, ACIDS...

OOOOOH...

IT ALL BEGAN AT KRUSTYCO PLAYTHING ASSEMBLY PLANT #9 IN SHANGCHOW, CHINA."

"THE PLACE WAS A **SMORGASBORD** OF SAFETY AND HEALTH VIOLATIONS AND A DISASTER WAITING TO HAPPEN."

"LIKE THE **LEAD** PAINT THEY USED. **RADIOACTIVE** LEAD PAINT."

SEE HOW CAPITALIST CLOWN'S EYES **GLOW** WITH LAUGHTER!

"AND THAT'S JUST THE **BEGINNING** OF THE VIOLATIONS."

ENOUGH OF YOUR PRIDE! WE ARE **BEHIND** QUOTA! SPOILED AMERICAN CHILDREN DEMAND HIGHER QUANTITY!

I HEARD **THAT!**

YOUR ENTIRE **BACKSTOCK** IS TOXIC. IT WILL HAVE TO BE DISPOSED OF **IMMEDIATELY!**

EVERY TOY, CLOWN!

FEH.

AND WHERE ARE **YOU** TWO GOING?

UM...

THE NEXT DAY...

THIS IS THE ONLY WAY, KRUSTY. YOUR CHRISTMAS INVENTORY BURIED FOR A MILLION YEARS.

YOU MEAN A MILLION *BUCKS*. OY.

CREEPY.

HEY HEY!

HEY HEY!

HEY HEY!

HEY HEY!

HEY HEY!

HEY HEY!

HEY HEY!

THE LEGENDARY LANDFILL OF FORBIDDEN TOYS.

WHAT'S *THAT* MEAN?

THIS IS THE FINAL RESTING PLACE OF THE UNSOLD, THE UNSAFE, AND THE UNMARKETABLE.

LIKE "DON'T ASK, DON'T TELL" G.I. JOE.

HOW MANY TIMES HAVE *YOU* SEEN "WICKED?"

AND *ROACH FARM*.

ROACH FARM

OR SINGLE MOM MALIBU STACY.

NEW

MERRY CHRISTMAS, KIDS!

LOOK! *SANTA* BROUGHT YOU A ROBOT PUPPY!

THAT'S *OUR* DOG WRAPPED IN FOIL.

A DOLL-HOUSE MADE FROM A LAUNDRY HAMPER?

COOKIE DOUGH ACTION FIGURES?

EW... THIS IS MADE FROM *DAD'S* SOCKS.

WE GOT *HOSED,* LIS.

THAT AFTERNOON...

˧GRUMBLE˧... ˧GRUMBLE˧...

...˧CARP˧...

...˧GRUMBLE˧... ˧MOAN˧...

ARE ALL *YOUR* STOCKINGS EMPTY?

MY DAD GAVE ME HIS ROLLOVER MINUTES.

WE GOT ZILCH. ZIPPO.

NADA. ZERO.

MY PARENTS ARE *DIVORCED!* THIS WAS SUPPOSED TO BE MY *PAY OFF!*

GOD? WHY DID YOU *DO* THIS? *THESE* KIDS WEREN'T NAUGHTY. AND THIS PAST YEAR'S BEEN A PERSONAL *BEST* FOR ME.

MEANWHILE, OUT AT THE LANDFILL...

...THE PRESSURE FROM INSIDE HAS CAUSED STRESS FRACTURES IN THE CONCRETE.

THE HEAT FROM DEEP WITHIN THE CONTAINER MELTS THE SNOW...

...AND THE WATER REACHES THE SUPER-HYDRO-ACTION KRUSTY TOYS.

MILLIONS OF TONS OF PRESSURE BUILD UP FROM THE EXPANDING CLOWNS...

...UNTIL THE LANDFILL **BLOWS!**

KA-BOOM!

THE END

A GOURMET'S GUIDE TO FINE DINING

HERE'S MY ONE AND ONLY RULE FOR MASTERING THE SCIENCE OF FINE DINING: EAT EVERY MEAL LIKE IT'S YOUR LAST MEAL. TAKE NO PRISONERS, LEAVE NO LEFTOVERS, AND TELL THAT WAITERER HE CAN HAVE YOUR FORK WHEN HE PRIES IT FROM YOUR COLD, DEAD HAND.

Know Your Finger Foods

TURKEY DRUMSTICK? — YES!

CREAMED CORN? — NO!

PORK CHOP? — YES!

SOUP? — NO!

T-BONE STEAK? — YES!

SPAGHETTI AND MEATBALLS? — HMMMM. MAYBE...

The Buffet

The all-you-can-eat buffet. Mmmmm. This is man's finest hour. It's like Custard's Last Stand and D-Day rolled into one. First, get in close to the table and hold your position. Don't load yourself down with napkins, plates, and utensils... just arm yourself with one good, all-around fork or big spoon. Stand your ground and keep shoveling. And remember, it's every man for himself.

The 7 Basic Food Groups
Homer's Golden Pyramid of Foodly Delights

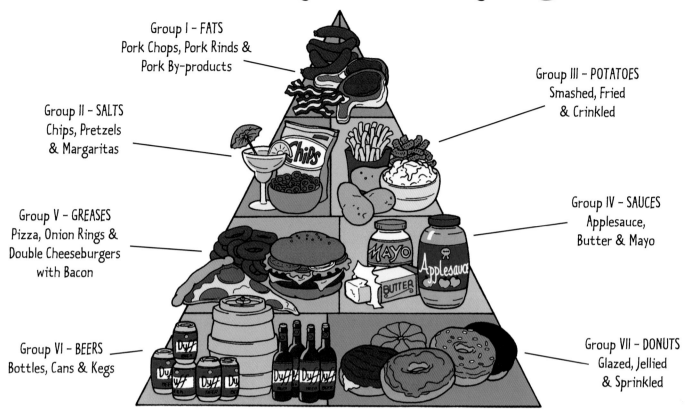

Group I - FATS
Pork Chops, Pork Rinds &
Pork By-products

Group III - POTATOES
Smashed, Fried
& Crinkled

Group II - SALTS
Chips, Pretzels
& Margaritas

Group IV - SAUCES
Applesauce,
Butter & Mayo

Group V - GREASES
Pizza, Onion Rings &
Double Cheeseburgers
with Bacon

Group VI - BEERS
Bottles, Cans & Kegs

Group VII - DONUTS
Glazed, Jellied
& Sprinkled

Ideally, there will be some seepage between food groups resulting in meals that are,
at once, fatty, salty, greasy, and beery in one delicious bite.

A Tip on Tipping

In olden days waiterers and waiteresses had to count on tips in order to eke out their meager existence. But now, thanks to the federally government insured guaranteed minimum wage law, waiterers and waiteresses make more money than most illegal farm workers. So, nowadays, tipping is no longer necessary. In fact, it has been my experience in fancy restaurants to have the waiterer find my tip to be downright insulting.

The Place Setting

At a formal table setting, you always get way more silverware than you
need, so don't be shy about pocketing any extra knives or sporks.

EARWAX
REMOVER

SPIT DISH

NOSE
WIPER

FOOD BOWL

BEER

BEER
CHASER

AFTER
DINNER
BEER

STEAK
FORK

PORK
FORK

DORK
FORK

SPILL
CATCHER

STABBING
TOOL

SOUVENIR
SPOON

MASHED
POTATO
SPOON

Lisa Simpson in READING NIGHT

IS EVERYBODY READY FOR MY "FAMILY READING NIGHT"?

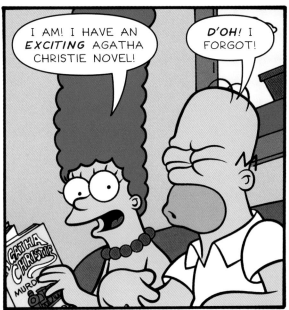

I AM! I HAVE AN *EXCITING* AGATHA CHRISTIE NOVEL!

D'OH! I FORGOT!

DAD!

IT'S OKAY! I'LL READ MY DUFF BEER BOTTLE LABEL!

"CONTAINS ONLY THE FINEST HOPS."

HEE, HEE! *HOPS*...WHAT A SENSE OF HUMOR THEY HAVE!

I'M READING "THE CAT WEARS A HAT"!

BART! THAT BOOK IS ONLY AT THE *FIRST GRADE* READING LEVEL!

EARL KRESS
STORY

JAMES LLOYD
PENCILS

PATRICK OWSLEY
INKS

ART VILLANUEVA
COLORS

KAREN BATES
LETTERS

BILL MORRISON
EDITOR

39

EARL KRESS
STORY

JAMES LLOYD
PENCILS

MIKE ROTE
INKS

ART VILLANUEVA
COLORS

KAREN BATES
LETTERS

BILL MORRISON
EDITOR

MARGE'S LIST OF MILDLY DISAPPROVED OF WORDS AND PHRASES

OBJECTS IN MIRROR ARE CLOSER THAN THEY APPEAR

SLIPSHOD

TOMATO

YOUR MILEAGE MAY VARY

DELINQUENT

PLEASE WAIT TO BE SEATED

PRICES SUBJECT TO CHANGE WITHOUT NOTICE

MATURE AUDIENCES ONLY

EXACT CHANGE ONLY

VIEWER DISCRETION ADVISED

DRY CLEAN ONLY

KID-VID

DO NOT REMOVE UNDER PENALTY OF LAW

ONE SIZE FITS ALL

WRONG WAY! STOP! SEVERE TIRE DAMAGE!

JUST HEAT AND SERVE

COMIC MISCHIEF

CRUDE HUMOR

MAY CONTAIN AGGRESSIVE CONFLICT AND/OR BLOODLESS DISMEMBERMENT

HOOCHIE, COOCHIE, TART OR FLOOZY

WENCH, SKEEZER, SKANK, OR BIMBO

DRAG AND DROP

BROAD, DAME, SKIRT OR REFRIGERATE AFTER OPENING

BLOOD AND/OR GORE

MALADJUSTED

SLAPDASH

CARTOON VIOLENCE

BELLYACHE

BALL AND CHAIN

LATCHKEY KIDS

EMPTY CALORIES

HAND WASH, DRIP DRY

MATT GROENING

43

BUSY BEE PUZZLES!

who BEE these?

Four Springfield residents are surrounded by bees! But can you tell who they are?

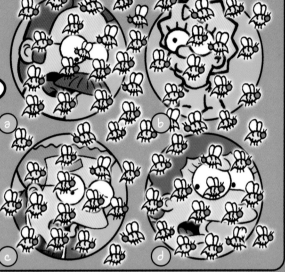

Count the spots!

HOMER WAS SAVAGELY STUNG BY A SWARM OF BEES. HOW MANY SPOTS CAN YOU COUNT ON HOMER IN THIS PICTURE?

Mrs. Hoover's BEE FACTS!

Bee clever!

- Bees have been making honey for around 150 million years!
- Bees have got five eyes.
- Bees can't recognise the colour red.
- A single hive contains about 40-45,000 bees.
- Worker bees live for only 28 to 35 days!
- A hive's temperature is about 93 degrees!
- Bees never sleep…

SPOT THE DIFFERENCE

Can you spot the five differences between these pictures?

Bart's Cool BEE FACT!

THE BUMBLEBEE USES 21 MUSCLES TO STING! AYE, CARUMBA!

MATT GROENING

45

OH, PLOW, WHERE ART THOU?

PATRIC C.W. VERRONE
& PATRIC M. VERRONE
SCRIPT

CARLOS VALENTE
PENCILS

VINNY NAVARRETE
INKS

ALAN HELLARD
COLORS

KAREN BATES
LETTERS

BILL MORRISON
EDITOR

I WONDER WHAT HAPPENED TO THAT PLOW.

FOR SALE

EXCUSE ME, BUT IS THIS THE SAME MR. PLOW SNOW PLOW MADE BY KOMATSU MOTORS, AS SEEN IN THE CHANNEL 92 COMMERCIAL AT 3:17 AM?

GEE, WELL, YEAH...YOU KNOW, I THINK IT IS.

FOR LE

THEN I WOULD LIKE TO PURCHASE IT. MIGHT I INQUIRE AS TO THE PRICE OF THIS FAIR-TO-POOR CONDITION ITEM?

YOU KNOW.. IT'S LIKE I WAS TELLING ANOTHER YOUNG COUPLE WHO WERE INTERESTED IN IT, YOU JUST CAN'T PUT A PRICE ON A BABY LIKE THIS.

FOR SALE

I'M SORRY, BUT YOU HAVE MISTAKEN ME FOR SOMEONE WHO DICKERS.

AW C'MON, GIVE OL' GIL ANOTHER CHANCE FOR A GIVE 'N' TAKE.

ARE YOU DEAF AS WELL AS DUMB?

I SHOULDN'T BE TELLING YOU THIS, BUT I DON'T WORK HERE. THE MANAGER JUST LETS ME SLEEP IN THE CARS.

THEN WILL YOU TAKE $100?

SOLD!

♪ HERE HE COMES! ♪

♪ HERE COMES, ERASER! ♪

♪ HE'S A DIAMOND ON WHEELS! ♪

♪ HE'S A DIAMOND, AND HE'S GONNA BEACH HAZING AFTER SUMMONED. ♪

♪ GHOST ERASER! GHOST ERASER... ♪

OH GOODNESS! TWELVE O'CLOCK! I'LL BE LATE FOR MY APPOINTMENT.

SEEMS LIKE A SHORTER WALK TO THE GARAGE THIS MORNING.

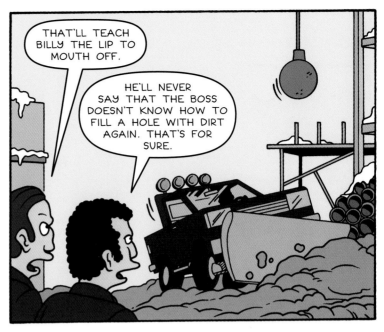

THE TRANSCENDENTALISTS AMONG THE MEN THOUGHT IT WAS A METAPHORIC EMBODIMENT OF THEIR SOUL, WHILE THE ROMANTICISTS FOUND IT TO BE AN EPIC ALLEGORY OF OBSESSION.

IT'S A SNOW PLOW. I'LL GIVE YOU $100 FOR IT.

SOLD!

HELLO, HERMAN, WHAT'S NEW?

JUST GOT AN ITEM IN WHICH I THINK YOU MIGHT HAVE SOME INTEREST.

WORLD WAR II VINTAGE KOMATSU SNOW PLOW

I KNOW THAT PLOW! IT CAN'T BE.

ABE? YOU OKAY?

DON'T WORRY, MEN. YOU'LL BE SAFE HERE BEHIND THIS SNOW BANK WHILE I GO GET HELP.

THE END

MOE PROBLEMS MOE PUZZLES

SZYSLAK SEARCH

Can you find these 10 Moe-related words in this Moe-centric wordsearch? Answers appear horizontally, vertically, diagonally, or backwards!

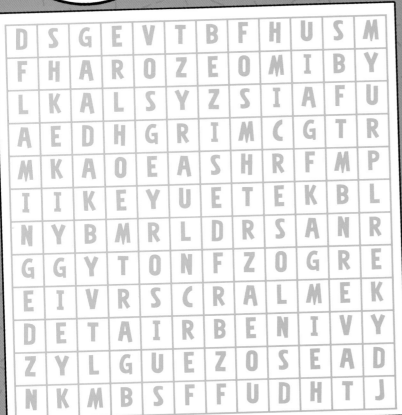

D S G E V T B F H U S M
F H A R O Z E O M I B Y
L K A L S Y Z S I A F U
A E D H G R I M C G T R
M K A O E A S H R F M P
I I K E Y U E T E K B L
N Y B M R L D R S A N R
G G Y T O N F Z O G R E
E I V R S C R A L M E K
D E T A I R B E N I V Y
Z Y L G U E Z O S E A D
N K M B S F F U D H T J

MOE TAVERN **LOSER** UGLY
DUFF **BEER** INEBRIATED
FLAMING
BACHELOR **SZYSLAK**

NAME THAT GUY?

Here is the name of a famous Simpsons character, but we've jumbled it up!
Can you figure out who it is?

LAZY SMOKES

SPOT THE DIFFERENCE!

There are FIVE differences between these two pictures. Can you spot them?

MATT GROENING

'Twas the Eve Before Christmas

by

Homer J. Simpson

'TWAS THE EVE BEFORE CHRISTMAS, AND ALL THROUGH OUR HOME NOT A SOUND COULD BE HEARD, 'CEPT A SAX-O-MO-PHONE.

THE STOCKINGS WERE HUNG ON THE MANTLE DOWNSTAIRS, WHEN MARGE ASKED ME...

HAVE YOU SEEN MAGGIE SOMEWHERE?

THE CHILDREN ARE NESTLED IN BED AS THEY SHOULD.

I SAID, KNOWING BART WAS STILL UP (TO NO GOOD).

SO MARGE IN HER HAIR SOCK AND ME IN MY SHORTS BEGAN SETTLING DOWN FOR SOME NAPPING...OF SORTS.

PATRIC M. VERRONE
SCRIPT

MIKE KAZALEH
PENCILS & INKS

ALAN HELLARD
COLORS

KAREN BATES
LETTERS

BILL MORRISON
EDITOR

WHEN OUT OF OUR BED
SHE JUMPED UP LIKE A FLEA, YELLING...

HOMER, YOU MUST PUT THE GIFTS BY THE TREE!

THE PRESENTS!

I GASPED, WITH A SLAP TO MY HEAD, THAT GAVE ME TO KNOW I HAD SOMETHING TO DREAD.

I'D LEFT THEM WITH GRAMPA, WHO GAVE ME A HASSLE WHILE MEETING HIM AT THE RETIREMENT CASTLE. THEN WE STOPPED OFF AT MOE'S, AND THE REST WAS A BLUR. NOW MY BRAIN COULDN'T TELL ME WHERE ALL THE GIFTS WERE.

AWAY TO THE KITCHEN I FLEW IN A PUFF, TORE OPEN THE ICE BOX AND THREW BACK A DUFF,

NEW PRESENTS I NEEDED TO FIND WITH GREAT SPEED LIKE, FOR LISA, THE PHONE BOOK...

'CAUSE SHE LIKES TO READ.

LITTLE MAGGIE WON'T MIND IF SHE GETS THE DOG'S BOWL. AND BART, HE DESERVES A BIG FAT LUMP OF COAL. BUT MARGE WON'T BE EASY TO FOOL WITH THIS TRICK...

THEN IT DAWNED ON ME...

I COULD DRESS UP AS ST. NICK!

AN OLD SANTA SUIT'S IN THE BACK OF MY CLOSET: I'D RENTED IT, KEPT IT, AND LOST THE DEPOSIT.

PARCHINTZY

MONOTONY

SCRAMBLE

IF "SANTA" SHOWS UP WITH THESE GIFTS THERE'LL BE GLEE. IT WORKED FOR THE GRINCH, SO HOW HARD COULD IT BE?

WHILE HATCHING MY PLAN THERE AROSE SUCH A CLATTER MUCH WORSE THAN THE CAT IN THE CRAWL'S PITTER PATTER.

I WENT TO THE BOY'S ROOM TO TAKE HIM APART. I PRACTICED MY ENTRANCE...

WHY YOU LITTLE-- BART!

BUT THE SOUND WASN'T THE CAT'S NOR WAS IT THE BOY'S. SOME JERK ON MY ROOF WAS THE CAUSE OF THIS NOISE.

I PEEKED OUT THE DOOR
TO SEE WHAT KIND OF THIEVES
WOULD BURGLE ON HOUSETOPS
ON CHRISTMAS' EVES.
BUT WHAT DID MY WONDERING
EYES CHANCE TO SPY?
IT WAS SANTA HIMSELF
WITH SOME ELK WHO COULD FLY.

NOW, DASHELL!
NOW, DAGWOOD!

HE CALLED ONE A VIXEN!

ON WHOSE-IT!
ON WHATS-IT!...
ON...(SOMETHING
LIKE) NIXON!

HE SLID DOWN THE CHIMNEY,
PAST THE FIREPLACE GRATE.

HE BETTER
BE CAREFUL. MY
INSURANCE IS
LATE.

LEAVING GIFTS 'NEATH THE TREE
WITH THE SKILL OF A CROOK.
HE SAID WHEN HE SAW ME...

NOW
YOU'RE OFF
THE HOOK.

I INVITED HIM IN
FOR SOME HOLIDAY GROG.
WE TOASTED EACH OTHER
WITH MARGE'S EGGNOG.

I ASKED HIM HIS SECRETS
FOR LOOKING SO SLIM.
HE SAID...

ALWAYS
WEAR COATS
LINED WITH
BUFFALO
TRIM.

WE LAUGHED AND WE GOSSIPED LIKE TWO MOTHER BEARS. THEN, TURNING TO LEAVE AS THE KIDS CAME DOWNSTAIRS, I ASKED...

SO, WHICH GIFT IS FOR ME, MAY I KNOW?

IT'S *YOUR* FAMILY.

...HE SAID, AND I BLURTED OUT...

D'OH!

SO TOGETHER WE SIMPSONS SAT DOWN BY THE TREE, AND WE BASKED IN THE LOVE...

...OF A BRAND NEW TV.

WJBK

CHANNEL 101

AND THEY HEARD ME EXCLAIM WHEN I BID THEM GOOD NIGHT...

MERRY CHRISTMAS TO ALL AND TO ALL...

SHUT THAT LIGHT!

The End

HAVE A BLAST
WITH THESE GREAT SIMPSONS BOOKS!

ISBN: 9781852865979

ISBN: 9781852866693

ISBN: 9781852867270

ISBN: 9781852867645

ISBN: 9781852868062

ISBN: 9781852869557

ISBN: 9781840230581

ISBN: 9781840231519

ISBN: 9781840234039

ISBN: 9781840235920

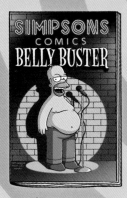

ISBN: 9781840237900

ISBN: 9781845760106

ISBN: 9781845762285

ISBN: 9781845764104

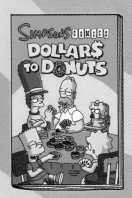

ISBN: 9781845767518

ISBN: 9781848562271

ISBN: 9781852868208

ISBN: 9781848565197